MW00898963

This book belongs to:

_____

A special thanks to Pamela Janovyak, and Samuel and Mary Wall
for your labor of love in helping me to get this book to print.
I love you! - Tracy

All Scriptures noted with "WT" are quoted from the Working
Translation in *A Journey Through the Acts and Epistles*
(copyright © 2006 by Walter J. Cummins. All rights reserved.)

I Speak in Tongues!

Written by Tracy Born

Illustrated by Tracy and Lillie Born

God gave me holy spirit
when I believed on His son.
I know I'm His child,
I know I'm born again.
I speak in tongues!

Just like they did
on Pentecost Day
I speak the wonderful
works of God!
The spirit gives me
the words to say.
I speak in tongues!

I speak in tongues every day.
God understands the words I say.
This very special thing I do
speaking secrets to God,
not to me or you.
I speak in tongues!

When I am alone
or if I get scared,
I can stop, I remember,
God loves me! He is here!
I speak in tongues!

So I speak in tongues all day,
I do it many times.
I'm talking to my Father,
it's quiet in my mind.
I speak in tongues!

I can speak in tongues,
interpret and prophesy too.
They're words from God
to edify you.
I speak in tongues!

I know God loves me
and His Word is true,
so I want to do
what He says to do.
I speak in tongues!

God gave me holy spirit
when I believed on His son...

That if you will confess with your mouth the Lord Jesus and will believe in your heart that God raised him from the dead, *then* you will be saved.
Romans 10:9 (WT)

Just like they did
on Pentecost Day...

Then they were all filled with holy spirit, and they began to speak in other tongues, as the Spirit was giving them [*the words*] to speak out.
Acts 2:4 (WT)

"Cretans, and Arabians. We hear them speaking in our tongues the magnificent *things* of God."
Acts 2:11 (WT)

I speak in tongues every day,
God understands the words I say...

In fact, he who speaks in a tongue does not speak to men but to God, because no one understands what he hears *himself speaking*. By the spirit, he is speaking mysteries.
1 Corinthians 14:2 (WT)

When I am alone or if I get scared I can stop.
I remember, God loves me! He is here!...

The spirit itself bears witness with our own spirit that we are children of God.
Romans 8:16 (WT)

So I speak in tongues all day, I do it many times!
I'm talking to my Father, it's quiet in my mind...

I thank God, I speak in tongues more than you all.
1 Corinthians 14:18 (WT)

I can speak in tongues,
interpret and prophesy too...

Wherefore, let him who speaks in a tongue pray that he may interpret
[*in the church*].
I Corinthians 14:13 (WT)

I know God loves me and His Word is true,
so I want to do what He says to do...

What is it then? I will pray with the spirit, and I will pray with the mind also. I will sing with the spirit, and I will sing with the mind also.
1 Corinthians 14:15 (WT)

For more information about speaking in tongues, or anything else in this book, you may contact the author at:
Trborn1@gmail.com
or
Pittsburghbibletf@gmail.com

CPSIA information can be obtained
at www.ICGtesting.com
Printed in the USA
LVHW072228180421
684863LV00031B/1184

9 780578 864051